A bit about n

My name is Lily Murphy, I am an autistic 17 year-old girl. I was 9 when I was diagnosed with autism. It was much more obvious that I had autism in my first years of school. I used to scrunch up my hands up and slap myself, on my legs and chest, when I got excited without me even realising I was doing it! My teachers and mum picked up on this, as well as my coordination issues and how I processed information, which was a lot slower than other neuro-typical children. This pushed my parents to get me tested for Autism. As I've grown older, I have learnt how to handle it better. Some people can't always tell that I have autism, as I don't openly show signs most of the time.

I live in a small village called Greasby, located on the Wirral, Merseyside (between Liverpool and North Wales). I have lived there my whole life and I live with my older brother, mum, step-dad, and my two dogs. Even though I don't live with my dad, me and my brother stay with him every other weekend and it has been this way since I was 2 years old. He used to have to travel from London every time until him moving back to live by us in a nearby village called West Kirby in 2020. I also have a half-sister, who lives with her boyfriend nearby too.

I have found having autism very challenging at times, especially since I started high school. The pressure went up another level from being in primary school, where it was much smaller, and there were less children and I felt more secure. I couldn't cope with it at first. It took a few years in high school before I could cope with the pressures and even then, I could only just about cope!

Now I am in 6th form, having done quite well in my GCSEs, I am managing much better and enjoying my education a lot more.

My personal interests are:

- art/creating, making cards,

- bookmarks, crafts.

- video games,

- tv,

- reading,

- singing,

- spending time with my dogs, family and friends

- volunteering at a local animal rescue centre.

What is Autism?

If you don't already know what autism is, it is a condition that affects your social and communication skills as well as many other things. It usually affects your: social skills, communication, learning progress, speech, and your behaviour etc.

There is a large autistic spectrum which goes from having very mild autistic traits, to more severe traits.

If you have not yet been diagnosed with autism, here are some common symptoms to look out for which might be a sign that you are autistic: (if this is the case then I suggest you getting tested for it):

- Avoiding eye contact with others.

- Getting very un-settled and upset if you don't like a certain, taste, smell, feeling or sound.

- Repetitive movements such as: flapping hands or rocking your body back and forth (called stimming).

- Not talking as much as others.

- Repeating the same phrases that you've recently said or someone else has recently said (called Echolalia).

- Not understanding what others are feeling and why they are feeling that way. (they find it hard to read people's body language and expressions).

- Finding it hard to express how you are feeling.

- Liking a strict routine and getting stressed if there are any sudden changes to your daily routine.

- Having a very passionate interest in a subject or activity.

- Taking sayings and phrases very literally e.g. break a leg.

One of the main areas that Autistic people have difficulty is social skills - how we interact with others.

Social difficulties

It is extremely common for autistic people to have difficulty socialising, therefore it is so important to not feel alone if you suffer with this. I have difficulties communicating with my friends and family on a regular basis and I know how upsetting it is to have to deal with this. Some examples of this are:

- I don't always have a filter of what is relevant or appropriate to say to someone. This means that I can sometimes come across as being rude but to me it seems perfectly fine to discuss things others may think is inappropriate.

- I find it hard to keep up with the latest trends, meaning it's sometimes difficult to make conversation with my friends. To seem less 'out of it', I sometimes play along pretending that I do know what they are speaking about when, in reality I have no idea what they are going on about!

- When I ask a lot of questions when watching a film or listening to a story, people get annoyed at me for pestering them. However, it's just because I am easily confused and I'm also a very curious person, which I can't do much about.

- I usually find it quite hard to have the first word with someone I have never met before or seen in a while as I feel I am going to say the wrong thing and make things awkward!

- I have found that my emotions aren't always shown in my facial expressions. So sometimes I'm feeling relaxed, but people ask if I'm ok because my face looks worried! Or I look like I am smirking when something is quite serious/sad.

- I usually like to always tell the truth and be honest as I fear that I will get found out and then lose a friend and I already find it hard to make new friends as it is. I therefore find it extremely upsetting when I lose a friend, especially if I've known them for a while.

- I am often the last person to be chosen, in a class with none of my usual friends in, when the teacher wants you to get into groups. When the teacher must put me with a group, the people in the group usually snigger at each other as they see me as a disadvantage to their group. This obviously quite upsetting for me, but I just try to ignore it.

- People think I am weird as I sometimes I flap my hands in excitement. This is an example of stimming and I have done this ever since I was little. Lots of people don't realise that is quite normal to do this as everybody has some sort of self-stimulating behaviour e.g. biting nails, clicking knuckles and twirling hair. It actually helps calm me.

Useful tips if you have experienced anything similar to what have mentioned.

- Be honest with your friends and family and if they don't already know, tell them that you have autism. Don't be worried about being open with your family and friends as if they don't react nicely to you telling them, then they are not nice people as there is nothing wrong or bad about having autism. It just means the autistic person sees and reacts to the world differently. The fact that you've had the confidence to be open about your struggles is an achievement in itself and if they don't see that then it's not worth giving them your time.

- Don't change who you are to fit in as it's not worth the hassle and you'll only come across as being fake. Not being up to date with the latest trends is ok. Be honest with your friends and ask them to explain it to you. The most important thing is to just be comfortable with who you are as a person. You will always find someone who understands you and is kind to you at some point in life, so there's no need to worry about trying to attract friends. It's just all about being patient and wait for that time to come.

Dyspraxia and Irlen Syndrome

Dyspraxia

People with autism can commonly also have other neurological or developmental conditions for example: ADHD, Dyspraxia, OCD, Irlen syndrome and sensory processing disorder.

I also have Dyspraxia (also known as developmental co-ordination disorder). This is a condition which means I have trouble developing my co-ordination skills. When I was younger my mum noticed I couldn't: bounce or catch balls easily, skip, balance well, learn how to work a swing in the park (I didn't know when to swing my legs back and forth), I also had difficulty holding my knife and fork and my pen/pencils at school. Something that is part of having

Dyspraxia is Proprioception, which is all about being aware of where your own body is in the space around you. For example, I used to be really scared when people would stand on the edge of a cliff, that they will fall off and I would fall into the road if I was too near to the curb.

When I was assessed for Dyspraxia, I had to stand on a mat and close my eyes and balance and stand on an imaginary line. When I did this, I fell to the ground as I couldn't tell where my body was, and I thought I was going to fall off something.

As a result of this, I was given some lessons on how to co-ordinate my fine and gross motor skills. For my fine motor skills, I was taught how to hold and use: pens, pencils, scissors and how to pick up and move small objects from one place to another. For my gross motor skills, I was taught how to: bounce, throw and catch balls and beanbags. I also had to learn how to balance by stepping on imaginary stepping-stones across a room.

This all helped me to improve my co-ordination skills. This is only a brief explanation of my Dyspraxia and the difficulties I faced and still sometimes still face today. Some other examples of my past and present difficulties are:

- Participating in competitive sport e.g. in PE lessons I don't like to take part in case I let the team down by making mistakes.
- In games like tennis, I find it hard

to co-ordinate my eye and hand movements.

- When I was learning how to hold and use a pen/pencil, I had to put a rubber grip on the pen or pencil to help hold it in place.

- In school I did my work on a writing slope and I sat on a bobbly plastic cushion, so I was more in contact with my surroundings.

- I found it hard to keep up with the fast dance routines when I used to go to dance classes. Unfortunately in the end I had to give it up.

- I didn't learn how to ride a bike till I was about 8 years old.

Irlen Syndrome

When I was about 9 years old, I got diagnosed with Irlen syndrome as my mum and my teachers recognised that I was reading slower than others. Initially they thought it may be dyslexia, however it turned out to be Irlen syndrome. It affected me by the words on the page moving around, causing me sometimes to re-read or skip some lines in the text I was reading. When I got special-coloured lenses in my reading glasses, my reading speed increased by 30%. Now I'm in high school I feel to self- conscious to wear my glasses, so instead I use a coloured overlay which I place on top of the text I'm reading.

Sensitivity

- **Physically:**
  Being sensitive to certain materials and surfaces is a common autistic trait and it is completely normal if you are affected by this. Even some neuro-typical people have specific materials that they get irritated by. I mainly struggle with my sensitivity when wearing some clothing materials but also some other things too. These include

- Labels.

- Sequins/studs.

- Lace.

- Buttons.

- Sometimes wool.

- Some seams.

- I can't wear earphones as they hurt my ears after wearing them for a while and they often fall out of my ears which annoys me.

- Something that is usually very rare in teenagers is that I can't stand fizzy drinks. The reason for this is I just hate the fuzzy feeling on my tongue, which just ruins the whole drink for me!

- I am very sensitive to noise e.g. screaming and loud music

- I also recently found out that I am quite sensitive to light as I was struggling to get to sleep and I noticed that once I turned my little lamp off I fell asleep a lot quicker.

- I hate needles/injections as I find them extremely painful, uncomfortable and distressing.

Useful tips to hopefully help you deal with your physical sensitivity:

- If you are sensitive to clothing labels then make sure to try and cut them out, the best you can, so you can no longer feel the scratchiness of the label.

- Let your family and friends know what you are sensitive to, so then you can be sure that they won't buy you anything that will irritate you.

- Wear a vest /stretchy top under

any top that includes any irritable materials e.g. a top with sequins on it. Then the annoying material hopefully won't affect you any more as it won't be in direct contact with your skin.

- Try wearing noise cancelling headphones to block out noise.

- For any injections or blood tests, you could ask for the area to be numbed with numbing cream.

Emotionally:

It is also quite normal to be emotionally sensitive whether you have autism or not. The quote "sticks and stones may break my bones, but words can never hurt me" isn't true as insults can hurt you just as much as getting something physically thrown at you. Insults can sometimes cause more harm than physically getting hit or punched, as the unkind words can get stuck in your head, and you then start to believe them. This is a form of bullying and should not be tolerated as it is most certainly going to affect your self confidence and self-esteem.

Here are some examples of what I struggle with emotionally:

- I hate disappointing someone or getting told off by someone as I always put other people first and before myself, as I care about others a lot and what they think of me.

- I struggle with anxiety due to many difficulties I have mentioned.

- I'm quite self-conscious, as I know I don't always "fit the norm".

- I get very upset and distressed if someone is saying unkind things about me behind my back.

School

As I mentioned earlier in the book, I've found high school quite hard to cope with. Being autistic isn't easy as the world isn't made for us, so we have to learn how to adapt to our surroundings. This is by no means an easy task, especially with school, as there are so many stressful and unsettling aspects to take in, these include:

- Change (the seating plan is often changed by teachers and there is sometimes a room change which creates a lot of uncertainty), people with autism don't like change of routine.

- Confusing and complicated content

to learn and remember which are covered very quickly, not always allowing me time to process the information.

- Short deadlines.

- Uncomfortable school uniform.

- Loud disturbing noises in and outside class.

- Lots of pressure with tests.

- Finding a loyal group of friends to hang out with at lunch and break time.

However, there can be good things about school, as it is obviously very important to get an education. Also, your day is structured. This is a big benefit for autistic people as we usually like to have a routine, so we know what we are doing every minute of the day.

Useful tips to hopefully help with issues at school:

- Inform your school about your problems as I'm sure there will be changes they can make to help you as an individual adapt to your surroundings, and with your learning; so your school life is that bit better.

- Make a revision timetable if you've got tests coming up so then you don't feel as overwhelmed as you'll have it all planned out.

- Ask to be told in advance of any tests so it does not come as a shock and disrupt your routine.

- Sit as far away from the noisy and disruptive children in class as possible, so then you can concentrate more easily.

- Agree a system with the class teacher to highlight you are struggling/feeling stressed. I have used a "green" and "red" card system in the past. I just hold up the red card which alerts the teacher I would like to leave the room. There are other less obvious ways to flag it to your teachers too.

- Be open with your friends, explain how you feel and what you may experience differently to them, also what upsets you. **If you don't tell them they won't know.**

<u>Anxiety</u>

Anxiety is a recurring emotion characterised by feelings of tension and worry. It usually involves intrusive thoughts entering your head that cause you to feel this way. (I learned this through my CBT work). I've struggled with anxiety on and off for most of my life now, especially since I've been in high school. It is known for autistic people to not always show that they are feeling quite distressed and anxious. This is especially true for girls, who mask their feelings. This is because some neuro-diverse people don't always know how they are feeling so they don't see the need to ask for help. If you can't explain how you feel, maybe try and drawing it out instead.

If you think that you are experiencing anxiety then here are some examples of physical and mental symptoms to look out for, that are common in people with anxiety:

- Sweating.
- Racing heart.
- Heavy and fast breathing.
- Hot flushes.
- Dry mouth.
- Lack of energy.
- Dizziness.
- Stomach problems including stomach aches.

- Experiencing lots of negative thoughts.

- Uncontrollable overthinking.

- Difficulties concentrating.

- Feeling panicked.

- Feeling irritable.

- Feeling on edge and on constant alert.

- Struggling to get to sleep.

- Changes in appetite.

If you are struggling with high levels of anxiety on a regular basis, I recommend looking into Cognitive Behavioural Therapy (CBT). This really helped me to think more positivity and recognise my thinking patterns. What is also made me realise is that it is my thoughts making me anxious, and this was causing me to feel bad. If I could change the way I think about things, then it can help me feel less worried and anxious. For example, if I was about to sit a test, I would get all worked up as I thought I would fail, but CBT made me challenge this thinking. It made me ask "what makes you think this"? "What is the evidence for this thought"? "Have you done really badly in the past?". I wrote these down a few times I had felt anxious. Usually, the answers and evidence did not support my worries. Once I realised this, I did not get as anxious.

Some common causes of anxiety in neuro-diverse people are:

- Change in routine.

- Upcoming exams.

- Sensory overload– this happens when something around us overstimulates one or more of our senses. e.g. loud noises and bright lights.

- Hormonal.

- Loneliness.

- Trouble at home or school.

- Feeling left out/ like you don't fit in (not understanding social norms or not keeping up with the latest trends).

Other useful strategies and tips to help you cope with anxiety:

- Deep breaths.

- Calming apps such as: Headspace, Calmony and Mindshift.

- Creating a sensory soothing box (nice smelling products/essential oils, creating a happy memories album on your phone or whatever device you may have, stress ball and head/earphones).
- Make sure to be prepared for upcoming exams e.g. creating a revision timetable (visual/written), making mind maps or flash cards and watching videos – see image on following pages.
- Use CBT techniques such as the CBT judge (more about this in a few pages).

- Tell friends and family how you are feeling as it is sometimes best to get things off your chest. If you are not quite sure how you are feeling but you know something is not right, don't bottle it up, still tell someone as they could be able help you.

- Hold ice cubes/ splash some cold water in your face as it stops you thinking about your thoughts and worries as you are more bothered on the coldness of the ice in your hands/cold water on face.

- Distract yourself by doing something you enjoy such as: going on a walk, baking something, drawing/painting something, watching a movie and having a bubble bath.

- Challenge your worries by using a pad like the one I use. (see image on following page).

- Buy some affirmations cards (positive statements and beliefs – we can retrain our brains to think positively by repeating these) or write your own that you can read to yourself.

- Write your worries down and re-visit them a couple of days/weeks later and cross them out if you are no longer worrying about them. This proves to yourself that your worries and thoughts change and that you can let go of them.

What am I worried about pad?

including other activities I need to fit in.

A useful CBT method is what I call the **CBT judge**. It is where you imagine that you are going to court to put forward one of your worries. Judges always need evidence of your statement. Using this technique you ask yourself is there any real evidence of this thought or worry actually happening? If not, you can let go of that worry but if there is then you need to take action to prevent the situation from happening again.

CBT Judge

<u>Fears</u>

It is completely natural to fear things in life. Every individual is fearful of many different things. Things that I fear are:

- Failure.

- Big spiders.

- Heights.

- The dark.

- Death.

- Wasps and bees.

- The more severe fears that people can have are called Phobias. I am fortunate to not have any, but some common ones include:

- Claustrophobia- fear of confined or crowded places.

- Acrophobia– fear of heights.

- Aerophobia– fear of flying.

- Arachnophobia– fear of spiders.

- Astraphobia– fear of thunder and lighting.

- Autophobia - fear of being alone.

- Hemophobia– fear of blood.

- Hydrophobia– fear of water.

It is all about trying to conquer your fears and phobias by facing them head on. Once you familiarise yourself with what you are fearing, you will start to become less afraid of it. However, this isn't always the case as sometimes once that fear gets into your head and scares you, then it's very difficult to let go of this fear.

Having autism also adds to this as our brains are wired differently to neurotypicals, so we experience fear differently (some say more severely). Therefore, we try to avoid doing activities that will be fearful to us. As the saying states fight or flight, we can either stand up to our fear and fight it or run away from our fear.   However, most of the time it is impossible to avoid everything that scares you, so when you have to come into contact with it, it is more of a shock than if you familiarised yourself with it, like I discussed above. An example of this is that I used to have a big fear of the dark but now my fear of the dark has decreased as I've been in a lot of dark places and have started to get used to it. It was only recently that I've been able to sleep in the dark when before I had to have a little bedside lamp, so this is proof of this. This has made me feel proud that I have overcome this fear and will make me more likely to challenge my other fears. A way to looking at dealing with your worries is using the **fight or flight analogy.**

You can either get scared by your worries and try and get away from them or you can stand up and challenge your worries, making them disappear.

Run away or face worries?

Run away from your worries:

Stand up to your worries:

Inspirational Quotes

I can't control the thoughts that pop into my head, but I can change my focus and whether I choose to believe them or not...

It is only you who knows how to love yourself completely...

Call yourself bad names for long enough and your mind will start to believe them – luckily this also works for good names too...

Don't feel bad about making mistakes, it's how we learn in life...

You're not alone. There's always somebody cheering you on and somebody who understands how you feel...

Positive Affirmations

Your friends and family are so proud of you...

You've got what it takes to be brilliant and positive...

I can and I will get through these hard times...

It is ok to feel worried as everyone feels this at some point in their life and it will always pass– you just need to be patient...

You don't have to solve all your problems all at once...

Today is going to be a really great day...

In Summary

Many people see having autism as a bad thing. However, this is certainly not the case. There are many benefits to having autism and these include:

- Having a different and unique view on things in life. I can spot things or challenge things that others don't.

- Having a real strength in a subject or hobby such as: drawing or photography– some autistic people have a photographic memory which results in them having an extraordinary memory.

- Being a very visual thinker, therefore having a very creative imagination.

- Able to concentrate for a long

period of time once motivated and focused on a specific task that interests and excites you.

- Being perfectionists, meaning that many autistic people produce amazing things such as: art work, robots and wooden sculptures etc.

- Being very inquisitive and wanting to understand their surrounding more.

- If you have been recently diagnosed with autism, I would suggest you joining autistic groups so then you can meet people who share similar autistic traits. This would hopefully make it clear to you that you are not alone, and it is normal to feel and act in the way that you do. It will also help you develop your social and skills by interacting with people in the group and taking part in activities.

I hope you have found this book helpful, and it has made you feel more confident within yourself. The reason I wrote this book was to share my experiences that autistic people can maybe relate to and find comfort from.